Potty Poets

Electric
Knickers

Electric Knickers

Potty Poems
to Power Your Pants

by

Andrew Collett

Illustrated by
Paddy Palgrave

The King's England Press
2001

ISBN 1 872438 69 5

Electric Knickers is typeset by Moose Manuscripts
in Comic Sans MS 14pt and published by
The King's England Press Ltd,
Cambertown House, Commercial Road, Goldthorpe,
Rotherham, South Yorkshire, S63 9BL

Printed and bound in Great Britain by

Woolnough Bookbinding
Irthlingborough
Northamptonshire

Foreword

This book, and my previous three collections, are all about getting children to pick up a reading book, to establish the reading habit, to generally get children to see reading as something which can be enjoyed.

So, thank you for the support of so many schools, festivals and children around the country. I'm delighted that my other collections are now firm favourites with so many people - big and small.

Dedications

This book is dedicated to my mother and her tremendous bravery.

Not forgetting, of course, my wonderful wife and son, Deborah and Toby, who have to put up with my wild nights of cocoa-drinking and biscuit-dunking.

Thanks go to my father, about whom so many of the poems are written. Without his dirty ways, disgusting habits and generally odd behaviour this book would not exist.

Finally, thanks to EVERYONE for buying so many copies of my previous revolting rhyme collections! There must be a lot of strange people out there!

Electric Knickers

Electric knickers
are the craze,
you can keep them on
for days and days.

Turn them up,
nice and slow,
and watch your bottom
start to glow.

Plug them in
on the hour
to give your bottom
extra power.

So come on people
everywhere,
it's time for electric
underwear!

POoooooMM!!

Snog the Dog

My mum kisses our dog
right on his nose;
how this can happen
nobody knows.

For with that smelly breath
and dribbling rear,
we think our dog's a saint
to even come near!

Blow Up Your Bottom

Blow up your bottom
before it goes rotten,
before it goes
gooey and grey.

Set it alight,
go on, do it tonight,
and see what
the neighbours say.

Stick in a rocket
inside each pocket
then watch
and stand quite clear.

You'll light up the sky
in the blink of an eye
with one wild
revolving rear.

Revenge of the Lampost

A dog one day saw red
when a lampost
bent down its head,
not to be polite
or say good night,
but to piddle on him,
instead!

Use Your Teddy Bear as a Toilet Brush

Use your teddy bear
as a toilet brush,
stick it down
with the very first flush.
There's nothing like
its hair or skin
to clean right round
your dirty rim.

Wriggle it slowly
from left to right
and hope that it
puts up a fight,
for wriggling, giggling
teddy games
will soon get rid
of stubborn stains.

The Queen's Blister

The biggest blister you've ever seen
belonged once to our Royal Queen
who, one day, when out at court
had the most delicious thought.

For, feeling rather ravenous,
and not wanting to cause a fuss,
she pulled at her royal shoulder
to show a blister, like a boulder.

And without waiting to be polite
she took the most enormous bite,
chewing this blister, big and runny,
and pronouncing it, "Rather yummy!"

And as others gathered round
to listen to her slurping sound
she slopped that blister in a bowl,
for she couldn't really eat it whole.

But not wanting it to go to waste
she offered a servant a little taste,
saying, 'Have a bite, oh, please do,
of royal blisters you'll taste but few.'

And so not to appear rude
the servant gobbled this famous food,
dripping bits all down his chin
as he ate it all, except the skin.

But now he wanted to be properly fed
and quickly gobbled the Queen's head
and before anyone could protest,
he took her body and ate the rest.

So let this be a lesson to royal lasses,
don't offer favours to working classes,
they'll take advantage, if you do,
and probably will eat you too!

Arthur Wrightus

Don't let those false teeth fool you,
don't let that hair loss hide
the might of Arthur Wrightus
and that walking stick at his side.

He maybe seventy two,
he may have lost his teeth,
but inside that cardigan
there's a superhero underneath.

With just one gentle nod
of his old and trusty pipe,
Arthur's one hair stands straight up
and his long johns go all tight.

His hearing aid starts to crackle,
his slippers give off heat
as rockets on his raincoat
fire him from his seat.

And so he's off to save the world
in just a puff of smoke,
for good old Arthur Wrightus
is just that kind of bloke.

More Always Eat
Your Bogies

Watch your bogies
as they grow,
wait until they
hang down low.

Then peel them out
with a squeal
and enjoy a tasty
bogey meal.

Dandruff Delight

We're having dandruff delight
for tea tonight,
we're having spots
from our dad's head.

We've mixed it about
turning it inside out
until it goes
gooey and red.

We're going to eat
the crust from our feet,
we're going to have
a wonderful time.

With great green grubs
and tasty fat slugs
washed down with
bottles of slime.

The Heated Toilet Seat

Sit on our toilet
and feel the heat
coming from
the toilet seat,
it's a new idea
for toilet seating
which now comes with
central heating!

For central heating,
deep down low,
is all the rage
each time you go,
but beware,
oh, please do,
of spending too long
on your loo!

You're in bother
and big trouble
if your toilet
starts to bubble,
so jump off quick,
start to run,
unless you want
a boiled bum!

Dare to Sniff Your Underwear

Do you dare to sniff your underwear
when it's been with you for days?
At telling if it's no longer fresh
there must be better ways!

Couldn't you ask someone else,
someone you don't know so well?
Then they could have the job
of telling if your undies smell!

Wet Gravity for Boys

I can wee up a wall
even though I'm quite small,
I can wee nearly up to the top.

But then I get stuck,
I don't have any luck,
I'm always forced to stop.

For as I stand there
I see drips in the air
and so run right out of town.

For there's one little rule
I remember from school:
What goes up must
also come down!

Elephants in Underpants

Elephants in underpants
would look so silly;
just think of it - an elephant
in undies all frilly.

One great big bottom,
swinging from side to side,
in undies big enough
to fit a bus inside.

So come on you elephants,
with bottoms so very bare,
why not make everyone smile
and try some underwear!

Toenail Talk

Tease out your toenails
all flaky and fresh,
squeeze them and ease them
away from your flesh.

Chomp them and chew them
one after one,
and enjoy the taste
of toenail fun.

The Planet Nappy

Of all the places in the world
the Planet Nappy is the worst,
for here nappies are tested
to see if they might burst.

They're filled with bits and pieces
and shaken left and right,
then given marks out of ten
to see if they stay white.

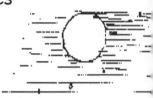

Detectors with flashing lights
tell if all's not well,
warning people to stand well back
if a nappy starts to smell.

And little men run around
with nappies hanging low,
testing for convenience
each time they want to go.

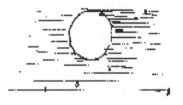

So let's all give thanks to everyo
for this nappy knowledge,
let's all clap our hands
for the famous nappy college.

But most of all let's all cheer
for Planet Nappy in the sky
and give thanks that its smells
are light-years from you or I.

The Toilet Test Pilot

The toilet test pilot
is there as a friend,
he's out to inspect
all dirty U-bends.

With goggles and helmet
he tries not to crash,
hitting your water
with a terrible splash.

On with his flippers
and radio control
as his plane sinks down
and into your bowl.

Twisting and turning
to make sure all's well,
looking for leaks
and any odd smell.

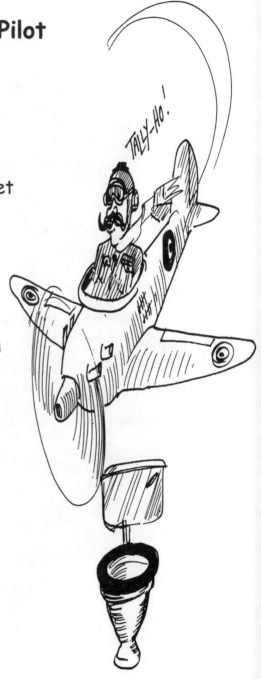

Then out with his armbands
and other odd things
as the pilot puts on
his water wings

So he can have
a moment or two,
paddling about
down in your loo.

Slipping around
on the inside
for all toilets make
a brilliant slide.

But what's really great,
what's a real plus,
is the chance to surf
on every flush.

So the job of the pilot
is a hard one,
but he still has time
for some toilet fun!

Bogey on a Stick

Push a pencil up your nose,*
wriggle from left to right,
scrape it down the sides
and squeeze it very tight.

Then quickly pull it out,
give it a lovely lick,
for there's nothing like the taste
of a bogey on a stick!

[*Don't try this at
home!]

Earwax Delight

Earwax delight
in the middle of the night
is a flavour so wonderfully right,
so run from your bed,
tip-toe to Dad's head
and try for an extra bite!

Sweet Feet Victory

You might have thought the Romans
filled us Brits with fear,
by scaring we foreign folk
as soon as they came near.

But we weren't scared of armies,
they didn't fill us all with fright,
their swords and great daggers
didn't keep us awake at night.

The only reason we gave in,
the only reason we would admit defeat,
is simply because those Romans
had such smelly feet.

For after marching over land
for days without a rest,
a thousand pairs of stamping feet
were never at their best.

And so this is the reason
behind the Romans' victory,
they just took off their shoes and socks
and the rest is history!

Always Eat Your Toilet Seat!

Always eat your toilet seat
after you have been,
for once it has been used
you just can't keep it clean.

Munch it from the middle
or cut it up in two,
serve it whole at dinner
so everyone can chew.

Pour on lots of gravy,
lick off lots of sauce,
have it as a starter
or a second course.

So come on everybody,
enjoy a special treat,
just put your lips together
and taste a toilet seat.

Our Dad

Our dad sleeps in the rabbit hutch
because of his terrible snore,
but Mum feeds him every morning
with toast and bits of straw.

Underpants in Orbit

Launch your undies
into space,
send them on
an underpants race.

Pump them up
from below,
then watch as they
start to go.

Racing at the
speed of sound
with pretty patterns
spinning round.

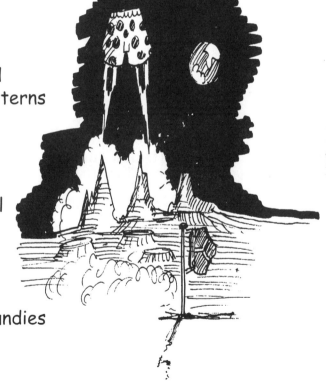

With rockets
in the elastic,
your undies will
look fantastic.

So let's all
have a race,
let's send our undies
into space!

Bang Goes Our Baby!

Our baby explodes
at least twice a day,
scaring old ladies
and big dogs away.
It likes to lie still,
tucked-up in its pram,
before suddenly going off
with an enormous great bang!

So just you watch out,
just you keep clear,
just you take cover
if a baby comes near.
For it might look all cuddly,
tucked up with its mummy,
but will blow you to bits
with one flick of its dummy!

32

Constipated Colin

Constipated Colin
didn't know what to do,
he spent his days
stuck in the loo
for Colin, you see,
just couldn't go,
for he had problems
down below.

Poor old Colin
was up each night,
trying hard
to put things right,
by eating figs
and bits of bran,
for this was clever
Colin's plan.

But it never worked,
he was ill
even after
a full fibre fill,
for poor old Colin,
as you know,
simply
couldn't GO!

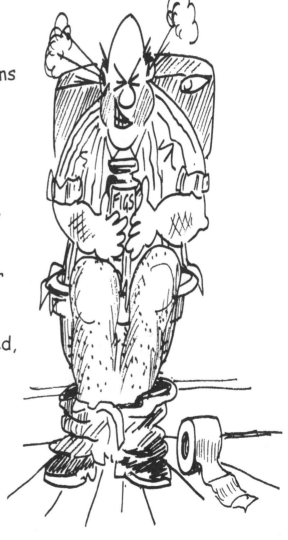

The horse now buried under this spot, enjoyed all his life but ran out of trot.

How Quick Can You Pick?

How quick can you pick your bogies?
Do they come out in pairs?
Are they always green and ripe,
or are they covered in hairs?

Do they slip right down your finger?
Do they stick like glue?
Are they always crusty on top
when you start to chew?

So how quick can you pick your bogies?
Can you shoot two at a time?
Do they go faster when they're dry,
or when they're covered in slime?

So how quick can you pick your bogies?
Let's dig deep in our skin;
come on people everywhere,
it's time you got stuck in!

We Wash in the Sewer!

We wash in the sewer
with bits of manure
and anything we can spot.

For it suits everyone
and we find it fun
when the water's greasy and hot.

It's a funny idea,
not to use water that's clear,
it's really strange we know.

But you can't beat the treat
of washing your feet
in someone's overflow!

Dribble Dribble

Our baby won't stop dribbling,
he's always on the go,
just where it comes from
none of us quite know.

We can fill two basins
and a bucket or two
with a day's supply
of our baby's gurgling goo.

There's dribble on his clothes
and sometimes in his hair,
we have to wade through lumps
of green stuff everywhere!

So what is the answer?
We just do not know
if we'll ever stop
our baby's foul flow!

The Convenience Cow

It's a model of convenience,
a creation full of surprises -
one cow who can deliver,
milk in bottles of all sizes.

But there's no nasty business
like an udder to try and find,
for fresh pints simply fall
from this cow's behind.

You can have it semi-skimmed,
cold or nice and hot,
you can have it pasteurised,
plain or golden top!

You can have an ice cream
with a topping or a flake,
ask this cow to do a dance
and then you've got milk shake.

It's a wonder of technology,
a real innovation,
it's a secret weapon
and a mighty strange creation.

Made by those farmer folk
it's always running at full throttle,
so the public can once again
buy fresh milk by the bottle!

Secret Weapon

The army has a secret weapon
never used before,
it's ready and waiting,
should there be a war.

It's not a brand new tank
with guns both big and strong,
but bags of rotten nappies
and their rather lovely pong.

So be warned, do take care,
everyone keep well back,
for there's little you can do
in a nappy attack!

But they won't harm or hurt you,
just make you feel unwell,
sending you running away
from their nasty nappy smell!

For they're the perfect weapon,
not deadly in any way,
but with their nasty niffs
enemies will always keep away!

Scabs

Scabs are often eaten
when crispy and hot,
by horrible little boys
who put them in a pot.

They're really inviting
and delicious to taste,
and with a crunchy scab
there's never much waste!

So gobble up scabs,
pick them with a pin,
and enjoy the flavour
as you peel off the skin.

Esmond on Holiday
(My Dad)

When ready for off
on our holiday
there's always one thing
which spoils our day.

For when in the car
we hear that cough,
as Dad decides
to take the wheels off.

We have to get out
and look impressed
as Dad picks a spanner
and strips to his chest.

"Watch and learn,"
he says in a growl,
as spanner hits foot
and he starts to howl.

Then three hours later
we're back in the car,
as Dad mutters something
about it being too far.

"We'll do it tomorrow,
we'll be way ahead,"
unless he decides to take
the engine out instead!

Cheese Between Feet

Cheese between feet
is always nice,
you can't buy it
at any price.

It's always best
when ripe and green,
so don't ever
keep feet clean.

Just be happy
in the know
that cheese is growing
down below.

And when it all
starts to smell
you'll know your cheese
is doing well.

But when people,
far and near,
suddenly start to
keep well clear

It's the moment
when it's just right,
so pull off your socks
and take a bite!

Dad and the Village Disco

When Dad started to dance
we just couldn't look,
for he'd always promised
to sit still with his book.

But it didn't take long,
in no time at all
he was strutting his stuff
at our village hall.

He fluttered his eyes
as if trying to flirt,
undoing one button
on his new nylon shirt.

He started to grin
and stuck out his chest,
as his tummy dropped down
and out of his vest.

But it was soon over,
it happened so fast,
everyone knew
that Dad wouldn't last.

He fell to the floor
in a big heap,
and, before the next song,
was quickly asleep.

The Cow Pat With Legs

A cow pat with legs
wouldn't fall with a plop,
but decide for itself
just where it should drop.

It could sit in the shade
to stay fluffy and light,
and go out for days
when the weather was right.

Then, just for fun,
it could turn up the heat
by jumping right under
everyone's feet.

And with a cow pat's
terrible pong
it could scare people away
so they never stayed long.

Cow pats with legs
are a wonderful idea
and the best way to keep
the countryside clear!

Rosehip, the
fortune-teller,
here lies dead,
she could have
saved herself
if she'd only
looked ahead.

Plumbing for Bottoms

Plumbing for bottoms
is a brilliant idea,
it's a much better way
of keeping you clear.

With pipes and pistons
to pump things round,
all sloshing about
with a gurgling sound.

With wipers and windows
keeping you clean,
and safety valves
to let off steam.

With tanks and taps
tuned to perfection,
ready for any
plumber's inspection.

So everybody shout
for this brilliant idea;
plumbing for bottoms -
to keep you clear!

The False Teeth Tournament

It's a brand-new craze
never seen before,
making false teeth
race on your floor.

They all line up,
motors revving low,
headlights flashing
so they know where to go.

Then they're off,
tearing round the track,
leaving tiny teeth marks
and streaks of black.

Shooting round the room
at a death-defying pace,
for all false teeth
just love to race.

Then suddenly it's over,
there's no longer any rush,
as the teeth take a pit-stop
for a wash and a brush.

But they'll be back,
just you watch this space,
for all false teeth
just love to race!

Growing Old Gracefully

Our mum's acting very strangely,
it's something we can't bear,
she's started to wear my sister's clothes
and do strange things with her hair.

She's even sending little notes
to Dad when he's alone,
and is always out at parties
and never off the phone.

She's using words like 'hip' and 'cool',
which she's never done before,
she's started sitting on Dad's knee
or a beanbag on the floor.

Our mum's acting very strangely,
we don't know what to do,
for she hasn't been the same
since turning forty-two!

Pigeon Power

Pigeon power is out to scare
so everyone cover their nice clean hair;
at aiming low they hit the spot
for pigeons are suddenly a brilliant shot!

With propellers, front and rear,
everyone knows to keep well clear
for these pigeons in the sky
have borrowed bits to help them fly,

With water pistols at the back
to give their goo that extra splat,
and helicopter feet to fly higher
with machine guns for rapid fire.

So do beware, everyone,
for pigeons are out just for fun;
they'll get their kicks on me and you
and shower the world with pigeon pooh.

Teachers' Socks

Teachers hang their socks
above the staff room door
to scare away small children
with a smell to make you roar.

And it always seems to work,
at any time of day,
for small children everywhere
know to keep away.

Which just leaves the teachers,
who never feel unwell,
for everyone knows that teachers
have no sense of smell!

Cow Pat on Toast

What I like most
is cow pat on toast
it's so delicious to taste.

It's like peanut butter
left in the gutter
with added bits of waste.

Sloppy ones are best,
they beat all the rest,
they're so easy to pour.

For they hit the spot
when creamy and hot
and leave you wanting more!

Brother Question

Every time my brothers
start to mess about
they run away and hide
before my mum comes out.

So before she can find us
and pull us in for tea,
why is there only one brother left,
and why is it always me?

Nose Smell

A child who would never clean
grew nine noses where only one had been,
but with nine times the smell
he began to feel unwell
which was a lesson to him on hygiene.

Catapult Crazy

The Roman catapult was double the fun
for not only did it make the enemy run,
but was also used to transport a slave
whenever he chose to misbehave!

Green Fingers

There's a low rumbling
beneath our feet,
it's not a monster
wanting something to eat
but toilet waste,
rumbling below,
stuck in the pipes
with nowhere to go.

It's a real nightmare
for it's at a dead end,
blocked for good
at the first U bend,
but the pressure's building
so don't look up -
our garden has exploded
in a shower of slop,

Sending our greenhouse
high into the air
and changing the colour
of our neighbours' hair.
But they don't mind,
there's not much to say,
for their gardens needed
extra compost anyway!

Pink Flamingos

All flamingos keep a feather duster
underneath their sink
so, before they go to bed each night,
they can tickle each other pink!

Superhero Transport

You might think superheroes
drive a supersonic machine,
one with rockets and boosters
which really looks mean.

But you'd be mistaken
and wide of the mark,
for supersonic machines
are so difficult to park.

A battered three-wheeler
is what superheroes like best,
one that chugs and glugs
and sometimes needs a rest.

For a musty old banger
gives brilliant protection,
and is a super disguise
from enemy detection.

Of course it is packed
with superhero things,
like missiles under mud flaps
and wheels with wings.

It's even got a jacuzzi
and a real escape chute,
with a cocktail cabinet
stuck in the boot.

So next time you spot
a three-wheeler on show,
it will probably belong
to a superhero!

Our Dog Wears Lipstick

Our dog wears lipstick,
you can't miss
his round and wrinkly
rubber lips.

He puts it on
every morning,
ready to snog
if you start yawning.

He can give
the kiss of death,
with his dirty
doggy breath.

So do watch out,
you can't miss
our dog's round
and wrinkly lips.

Here lies
the body
of a wine
taster
from York,
he died
when hit
on the head
by a cork!

Waterlogged

Dad took the telly into the bath
to watch his favourite football team,
but rain stopped play right away
when the pitch filled up with steam.

Elephant Dung

It's the new craze,
it's great fun,
diving into
elephant dung.

It stops your skin
from going rotten,
keeping it like
a baby's bottom.

It cools you down
when you're hot,
and warms you up
when you're not.

It makes wrinkles
disappear,
and keeps your skin
nice and clear.

So come on now,
for a treat,
and sit beneath
an elephant's feet.

Just enjoy that
delightful drop
of elephant's dung
all nice and hot!

Babies and Bare Bottoms

Babies are revolting,
they've all had enough,
they're fed up with nappies
to catch their nasty stuff.

They don't want piles of paper
stuck around their bottom,
and not those fluffy towels
which always smell so rotten.

It would be much better
and really much more fun
if they could show their bottoms
to almost anyone!

So come on all you babies,
throw your nappies in the air,
let's all get together
and have bottoms that are bare.